365

CONNECTING
QUESTIONS

FOR FAMILIES

CASEY & MEYGAN CASTON

COFOUNDERS OF MARRIAGE365

Illustration: Sel Thomson
Typesetting: Melanie Etemadi
Back Cover Photography: Haylee Forster
Blended Family Questions by Kristie Carpenter

ISBN Paperback 978-1-7324358-4-1

Published in 2019 by Casey and Meygan Caston

To Kylie and Cordell and to all of your friends who come to our house and eat all our food. May you always remember to be inclusive to those around you and to love people where they are at.

To Doris, Haylee, Anna, Brandon, Mike, Elisha, Sel, Vanessa, Ryan, and Jordan. Your constant support and talent amaze us! We couldn't do this without you all.

CONTENTS

INTRO-
DUCTION

Congratulations on picking up a book that is going to create stronger connections in your family! With all the distractions of sports, hobbies, and technology, the years with our children can zoom past us. If we are not intentional, we may miss our opportunity to connect during these pivotal years. Being intentional in our conversations with our children is a tangible expression that proves our love to them.

Whether you use the questions in this book during dinner, when you tuck your children into bed at night, or while running errands around town, family time is vital. It will look different for every family, but there are so many benefits of spending time together. Here are just a few...

Stronger bonds of connection

Families that spend time together feel a strong connection to one another. Throughout the day, everyone lived separate lives disconnected from one another. Your time together allows for everyone to regroup and process their experiences in a healthy environment.

Increased social development

During family time our children listen to the words we use and are expanding their vocabulary. They are learning social cues on when they can speak and when to be patient and listen. Remember – we don't teach our children manners by telling them what to do or not do, we teach them manners by modeling appropriate behavior in and outside of the home.

Improved mental health

The structure and consistent rhythm of sitting down for family time creates security in the hearts of our children. Studies show that children provided with a stable foundation are more confident and better equipped to fight off depression and anxiety. It has also proven to increase grades at school – seriously.

Family time is the perfect setting for starting conversations, but how do we actually start those conversations? What questions do we ask that will get us past "How was school?" and those dreaded one-word answers? In our research, we never found a good collection of questions that we could consistently go back to and use. That was the inspiration behind this book. What follows are the questions that we have been using with our children in an attempt to strengthen the core of our family and raise better humans. As a result, we have seen more love, more security, stronger connection, and experienced more honest conversation during family time.

THE #1 WAY TO BUILD EMOTIONAL CONNECTION WITH THOSE AROUND US IS TO ASK OPEN-ENDED QUESTIONS.

In the answer, we discover each other's dreams, desires, preferences, values, fears, and perspectives. This is true for marriage and even more so in parenting. Any parent seeking to create stronger bonds of trust, respect, and love with their children, has to actively engage in this activity. But there is so much more that we communicate when we ask a question.

First, it shows our desire to know our children. It is our role as parents to initiate the relationship with our children, to take the first step in reaching out. This sends a strong message that our children have a place of belonging in the family and that they are worthy of being pursued. Having a sense of self-worth is one of the most powerful things that we pass down to our children. That confidence will give our children the strength to stand strong when peer pressure weighs on them to do something they know is wrong.

Second, asking open-ended questions shows that we are listening. There is so much noise coming at our children these days between school, social media, and video games, that they need space to process the complex world of emotions raging inside of them. Having a safe place to share their feelings is a great way to show how much we love our children. Modeling listening skills helps our children understand empathy in our self-absorbed, screen-centered world.

Not only do we get a fuller understanding of what our children are going through, but once they feel that they have been heard, it opens the door for them to listen to us. And if we have truly listened, it will give us better insight on how to parent our children the way they need to be parented. This book is an incredible way to teach your children about real life issues like bullying, boundaries, education, and most importantly, how to proccess their feelings and emotions in a healthy way. There are so many parenting models and methods offered out there that can be overwhelming. The golden thread throughout all those models is that we have to listen to our children and now you have the tool to get started.

One last thought. We believe this book has the power to create strong families, which will create safer communities for us to live in. Our children need to know that they do not have to do life alone, that we are there for them, and that they are worthy of being loved and respected. When children feel safe and loved, they grow up to be healthy and happy adults. Isn't that what we all want for our children? Whether you think you are doing a good job of parenting or could use a little help, this book will give you immediate and quick wins with your children that will make your job much easier!

HOW TO USE THIS BOOK

BY DATE

For each day of the year, there is one Connecting Question. Turn to the date of the year and ask the question listed. You don't need to start on January 1 - any day is a great day to start.

BY TOPIC

If there is something specific you want or need to discuss as a family, pick a question by topic using the index in the back of the book (see page 190).

BEST TIMES TO USE THIS BOOK

FAMILY DINNERS

Studies show that families who make sitting down together for dinner a priority are healthier, more connected, and happier. While it may not be realistic to have family dinner every night, it's good to calendar at least three nights a week where you are able to sit down together, pull out this book, and take turns asking each other the question of the day. *Bonus tip: if you or your kids struggle to step away from screens, get a basket and have everyone drop their devices inside before you sit down to eat.*

RUNNING ERRANDS

Since parents play part-time taxi driver, be sure to bring this book with you in the car (or even keep it there) and take turns asking one question a day. *Bonus tip: ask questions when your children have friends in the car as a way to model healthy connection for their friends.*

BED TIME

Many children are most talkative at bedtime. Maybe they're trying to delay going to sleep, but children often process their entire day right before bed. They can be more open to having deeper conversations in the evening. Lay next to them or sit near them and talk about the question of the day.

You can also use this book...

- When grandparents come over
- On vacation
- At those long swim meets
- While camping
- On road trips
- While you're relaxing on the couch
- In-between sports games
- Waiting at the doctor's office
- When friends come over after school and stay for dinner

PARENT GUIDE

Limit distractions. Make sure you silence your phones, turn off the TV, and are ready to give 100% of your time and attention to the conversation. Be an example to your children. Time is a precious gift.

Remember that this book provides opportunities to teach your children about new words, new perspectives, and new feelings. Use this time to broaden their vocabulary, worldview, and emotional understanding. Customize the questions, if needed, to pursue a much deeper conversation about the topic at hand. For example, if you are talking about bullying, ask follow-up questions about which words can be hurtful, if they have experienced bullying, what happens at school if someone gets caught bullying, or consider sharing an experience *you* had being bullied. Don't just ask the question and leave it there —try to find ways to draw out the heart of your child.

Use the *How Are You Feeling?* chart in the back of the book (see page 187). Most of us use the same five emotions when we talk about our experiences. It's time to expand your family's vocabulary and our chart will help you and your children explore and more clearly communicate your feelings.

Don't interrupt. Interrupting sends mixed messages like,

"My answer is more important than yours," "I don't have time for your opinion," or "I don't really care what you think". It is important to model what healthy communication looks like for our children so that when they grow up, they don't interrupt their friends, co-workers, and future spouse or children. At the core of it, interrupting shows we really aren't listening and defeats the whole purpose of this book.

Listen with empathy. Children need to be able to share their thoughts and feelings while being vulnerable and messy, knowing that they won't be judged, minimized, fixed, or ignored. Listening with empathy means that you validate what they're thinking and feeling. Rarely does fixing or offering advice make others feel heard. So, engage with your children's stories, ask clarifying questions, and allow them to share how they see the world, even if it's a little unprocessed. Listening is a major component of connecting as a family.

Ask clarifying questions. If your child shares something that causes confusion or they are having difficulty finding the words to say, ask these clarifying questions:

- How did that make you feel?
- Can you give me an example?
- Do you want to think about this question a little bit longer?
- Will you help me understand what you are feeling?
- Can you turn to the *How Are You Feeling?* chart and

point to what you are feeling? (See page 187)

- Will you repeat that again? I want to make sure I understood you.
- On a scale of 1-10, how important is this to you? *Tip: This is one of our favorite questions we use in our marriage to help us quantify how meaningful a topic is.*

Pay attention to how your children respond to each question. Each child is uniquely created with different strengths, different talents, different ideas, and different feelings. This book will help you learn more about your children and we are certain you will discover new things about them.

Don't forget to share your thoughts. When asking the questions, be sure to participate in answering too. Your children want to hear *your* dreams, *your* feelings, and the challenges *you* face as an adult. While some of the questions might not be relevant to you, you should be able to answer most of the questions in this book.

Have fun! We need to help our children learn to be silly and know that we, as parents, can be silly too. Many of the questions will cause laughter – a lot of it!

HOW TO DRAW OUT A SHY CHILD

Extroverts get their energy from being around others by talking, laughing, and sharing stories, while introverts get their energy from reading a good book, being alone, or connecting with a close friend. Asking the questions in this book might be overwhelming to an introverted or shy child. An introverted or shy child might feel put on the spot or pressured to answer in these moments. These children can be internal processors who need time to think before they share their thoughts, feelings, or ideas.

Here are some helpful tips to keep in mind:

- Remind your child that it is okay to take breaks from socializing if they feel overwhelmed.
- Praise your child for taking social risks.
- If your child's first response is, "I don't know," don't make it a big deal. Simply say, "Okay, we'll come back to you in a bit," and move on to the next person.
- Pay attention to your child's body language and tone. This will give you insight on how they are feeling during times of sharing.
- Check your own expectations of the conversation. It's okay to be introverted and important you don't force your child to be someone they are not.

- Help your child express their emotions. Turn to the *How Are You Feeling?* chart on page 187 and give them time to come up with a word(s) that expresses how they feel.
- Don't label your child introverted or shy. This can cause your child to feel flawed and discourage them from sharing.

FOLLOW-UP QUESTIONS AND PHRASES

"I don't know" is a common phrase children might respond with when answering some questions. It might be true – they might not really know how to answer the question. Or they have attitude and don't want to talk to you. Or maybe they don't want to sound stupid by answering incorrectly.

Giving a short "Yes" or "No" answer might also occur, in which case you might start feeling frustrated. Here you are trying to have a heart-to-heart conversation and the only thing your child has to say is one-word answers. In these moments, it's important to stay calm and not allow your child's stubbornness to get the best of you.

Here are some helpful phrases and questions to use if your child seems to always have a very short answer to questions:

- Tell me more.
- Why do you think that happened?
- How did that make you feel?
- So what you're saying is...
- Could you tell me more about that?
- That's rough. How can I help?
- What were you thinking and feeling in that moment?
- Do you need more time to really think about it?

Families that talk together, stay together.

1

JANUARY

JANUARY 1

What is one of your favorite memories we
have together as a family?

JANUARY 2

What do you do really, really well?
Does it come naturally or have you
had to work hard at it?

JANUARY 3

If you were your teacher, what would you do
differently in your classroom?

JANUARY 4

What music do you listen to that lifts your
spirit when you are feeling down?

JANUARY 5

Do you believe in second chances?
Why or why not?

JANUARY 6

If you could save your money to buy one item,
what would it be and why?

JANUARY 7

Would you rather wear your shoes on the wrong feet or wear your pants backwards? Tell a story about a time when you woke up late.

JANUARY 8

Do you ever pray? If so, how often?

JANUARY 9

If you were to switch places with someone in our family for one day, who would you choose and what would you do as that person?

JANUARY 10

What is your favorite season and why?

JANUARY 11

Which subject in school is your favorite to
learn about? Why do you love it?

JANUARY 12

Do you have difficulty sleeping?
If so, why do you think that is?

JANUARY 13

How can you tell when someone is angry?
How do people behave when they are angry?

JANUARY 14

Would you rather be the world's best
skateboarder or world's best surfer?
What is your favorite action sport?

JANUARY 15

What is something you could do to
help one friend tomorrow?

JANUARY 16

There are over 400 different ways to exercise.
Can you name at least ten different ways?

JANUARY 17

If you were to start a nonprofit
organization, what need would it solve in
our community or in the world?

JANUARY 18

Which people in your life are the most
supportive and will help you accomplish your
dreams and goals? How can you spend more
time with those people?

JANUARY 19

What type of weather best represents
your personality? Why?

JANUARY 20

Why do you think so many children and adults
have a fear of going to see the dentist?

JANUARY 21

Would you rather go to outer
space or to the bottom of the ocean?
What do you think you would find there?

JANUARY 22

What will you be doing at age 30? What job will you have? Will you be married and have kids? What kind of person will you be?

JANUARY 23

If you found a wallet full of money, what would you do with it and why?

JANUARY 24

What is on your to-do list that never seems to get done?

JANUARY 25

How are you doing in school? Are you working your hardest or putting in minimal effort?

JANUARY 26

When you make a mistake and hurt a friend, are you quick to apologize with your words and actions? Why or why not?

JANUARY 27

Who in our family is the most organized? Why do you think this person is organized?

JANUARY 28

Would you rather skydive or
scuba-dive? Why?

JANUARY 29

Who is the most interesting person
you have ever met? What made this
person so interesting?

JANUARY 30

What makes someone confident?
How do you know when someone is confident?

JANUARY 31

If you saw someone being bullied
at school, what could you do?

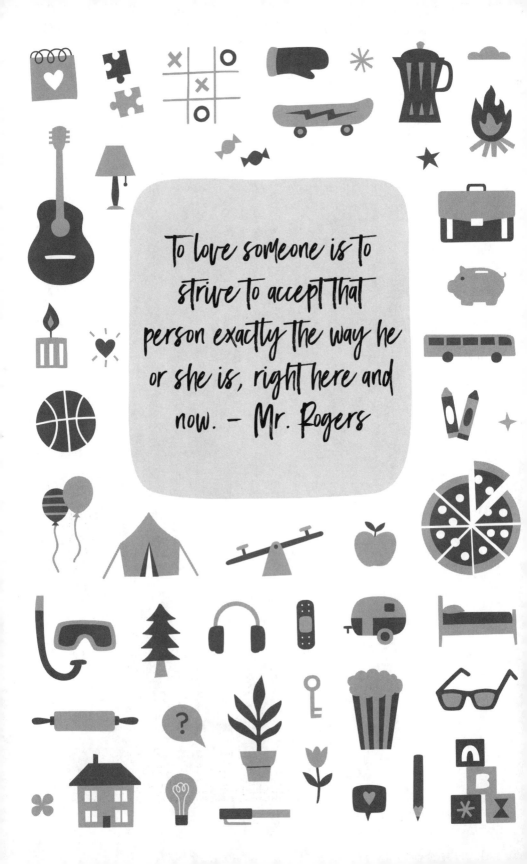

To love someone is to strive to accept that person exactly the way he or she is, right here and now. – Mr. Rogers

2 FEBRUARY

FEBRUARY 1

Would you rather be completely bald or
covered from head to toe in hair? Why?

FEBRUARY 2

How would you describe love?
Have you ever been in love with someone?
What did it feel like?

FEBRUARY 3

What is the difference between a
privilege and a right? Explain.

FEBRUARY 4

Why is it important for students at school to have positive relationships with each other?

FEBRUARY 5

What is your favorite kind of technology? Examples: video game devices, TV, phone, computer, etc.

FEBRUARY 6

How do you deal with a friend who is negative and in a bad mood? Is there anything you can do to cheer them up?

FEBRUARY 7

Would you rather live in a country that was
too hot all the time or too cold all the time?
Why? What would you keep with you to help
you cope with the weather?

FEBRUARY 8

What is something loving you
can do for someone you care for and
appreciate this Valentine's Day?

FEBRUARY 9

What is an object you always have with you?
Why is this object important?

FEBRUARY 10

If you could receive a gift card to any store or restaurant, where would you want it to be to and what would you buy there?

FEBRUARY 11

Who is someone you look up to as a role model and why?

FEBRUARY 12

Have you ever felt lonely? Will you tell me more about that?

FEBRUARY 13

Do you think you use your
time wisely? Why or why not?

FEBRUARY 14

Would you rather learn every musical
instrument or every language? Why?

FEBRUARY 15

Which five words best describe our family?

FEBRUARY 16

Are there any clubs that you want to be a part
of that are offered locally at your school?
Examples: math club, Boy Scouts,
Girl Scouts, drama, band, etc.

FEBRUARY 17

What is your favorite way to rest and relax?

FEBRUARY 18

What is the thing you like most about
computers and technology?

FEBRUARY 19

What was the last thing you bought?
Do you feel like it was an impulse buy?
Why or why not?

FEBRUARY 20

What do you like best: breakfast,
lunch, or dinner? Why?

FEBRUARY 21

Would you rather go skydiving or bungee
jumping or does your stomach get nervous
just thinking about it? Explain.

FEBRUARY 22

What is the greatest compliment
you could give someone else?

FEBRUARY 23

Who is the funniest person you know?
What makes this person so funny?

FEBRUARY 24

Tell me about a time when you were
disappointed. How did you deal with it?

FEBRUARY 25

What are some things your classmates
do that prevent you from learning?

FEBRUARY 26

What is one of your best qualities?

FEBRUARY 27

Which Olympic sport would you want
to learn how to do and why?

FEBRUARY 28

What gifts do you want for your
birthday? What would you like
to do on your birthday?

No one is perfect. That's why pencils have erasers.

3

MARCH

MARCH 1

Would you rather spend an entire day watching Harry Potter movies, Star Wars movies, or Marvel movies? Who is your favorite character in those movies?

MARCH 2

How would your best friend describe you?

MARCH 3

Which classroom activities or assignments help you learn the most?

MARCH 4

What are three things you want
to do during spring break?

MARCH 5

Name five things you would want with
you if you were on a deserted island.

MARCH 6

What brings you joy? What do you
do when you are feeling joy?

MARCH 7

Would you rather never have to
shower again or never have to brush
your teeth again? Why?

MARCH 8

Do you believe in God? What is he like?
How do you envision him?

MARCH 9

If you were given one million dollars to help
the planet, what would you do?

MARCH 10

Which chore do you actually
enjoy doing? Why?

MARCH 11

If you could change anything about our
family, what would it be and why?

MARCH 12

If you had to go to school forever, which
subjects would you want to study and which
teachers would you want?

MARCH 13

Do you consider yourself more
reserved or outgoing? Why?

MARCH 14

Would you rather stay your
current age or be 10 years older?
What would change if you were older?

MARCH 15

What is your favorite kind of weather? Why?

MARCH 16

How much time do you think the average kid spends using technology? Look it up online. How close were you?

MARCH 17

If you were to paint a masterpiece, what kind of art supplies would you use and what would you create? Which colors would you use?

MARCH 18

Has someone ever upset you but never apologized? Why do you think they never apologized?

MARCH 19

What is your favorite thing that Mom or Dad makes for dinner?

MARCH 20

How long would you wait in line for the world's best rollercoaster? Describe what makes this rollercoaster so special.

MARCH 21

Would you rather only be able to whisper or only be able to shout? What would your new speaking voice make you really good at?

MARCH 22

When you see something you really want, but do not have the money for, what options do you have?

MARCH 23

Of all the superheroes you know of, which superhero would you want to be and why?

MARCH 24

What do you think should happen when kids get good grades in school? Explain.

MARCH 25

When was a time you remember
feeling loved by a friend?
How did they make you feel loved?

MARCH 26

What is the scariest thing you have ever
experienced? What made it so scary?

MARCH 27

On a scale of 1-10, (1=never messy,
10=always messy), how messy is your room?
Why did you give your room that rating?

MARCH 28

Would you rather be super strong,
super fast, or super smart? What would
you do with your new skill?

MARCH 29

What is one thing you cannot
imagine living without and why?

MARCH 30

Who are your best friends and how much
time do you like to spend with them?

MARCH 31

What is something challenging you
have had to overcome? Explain.

The best thing about the future is that it comes one day at a time.
— Abraham Lincoln

APRIL 1

Would you rather stay up late or get up early?
What would be the world's best alarm clock?

APRIL 2

What is the hardest rule for you to follow at
school? What makes it so challenging?

APRIL 3

What is one thing you would NOT
do for a million dollars?

APRIL 4

What do you look forward to when
you wake up and why?

APRIL 5

When someone is nervous, what could you
do to help relieve their anxiety?

APRIL 6

If you opened a store, what would you sell?
What would be the name of the store?

APRIL 7

Would you rather visit the dentist
or visit the doctor? Why?

APRIL 8

What is something you want to
thank God for today?

APRIL 9

Which family member should do
which chore and why?

APRIL 10

How much time is too much time using technology? What are ways you can have a healthy balance?

APRIL 11

What do you enjoy giving people? Examples: your time, money, acts of service, gifts, kind words, hugs, etc.

APRIL 12

What are two things that make you feel scared? Explain.

APRIL 13

If you drew everything that came to your
head, what would you be drawing right now?

APRIL 14

Would you rather be really tall and skinny or
really short and strong? What new thing would
you do with your new height?

APRIL 15

When it comes to money, are you
a spender, a saver, or a little of both?
Why do you think that is?

APRIL 16

Is there anything you can do to get
better grades at school? If so, what?

APRIL 17

If you were outside for a whole day,
what would you do and why?

APRIL 18

What is your favorite thing about
spring time? Explain.

APRIL 19

What characteristics make
someone a good friend?

APRIL 20

What makes you feel energized and why?

APRIL 21

Would you rather be stuck outside or inside
for an entire 24 hours? What would you do
with your time? And no electronics!

APRIL 22

If you were in a play, what type of character would you like to be?

APRIL 23

What consequences do you think should happen when kids get bad grades in school?

APRIL 24

Why do you think police officers and firefighters risk their own lives to help others?

APRIL 25

If you could be invisible for a day,
what would you do?

APRIL 26

In what ways do you think technology
has improved our lives? Explain.

APRIL 27

Which one of your five senses do you use the
most (taste, smell, touch, hearing, and sight)?

APRIL 28

If you could be a famous person,
who would you be and why?

APRIL 29

Why do you think some people bully others?
Do you think these people might be in pain or
going through a difficult time? Explain.

APRIL 30

How do you like to help your
family and friends?

Ohana means family. Family means nobody gets left behind or forgotten.

– Lilo & Stitch

MAY

5

MAY 1

Would you rather never have to take another test in school or never get sick again? Why?

MAY 2

Are you being the best friend you can be to those who care about you? What are some things you can work on to be an even better friend?

MAY 3

Do you think telling the truth is always right even if it hurts someone's feelings?

MAY 4

What are three things that make
you feel sad? Explain.

MAY 5

If you could be a photographer for a day,
what would you take pictures of?

MAY 6

What is one thing you hope to learn
before the school year is over?

MAY 7

Would you rather go back in time
or skip ahead to the future? What date
would you set for your time machine?

MAY 8

Who can we pray for today?
How can we pray for them?

MAY 9

Does being generous mean giving away
everything you have? Explain.

MAY 10

What qualities or abilities
make someone smart?

MAY 11

In what ways has technology been
negative to our society? Explain.

MAY 12

If you could change anything about
yourself, what would it be and why?

MAY 13

In our family, who is the best cook?
Which recipe is your favorite?

MAY 14

Would you rather see everything in slow
motion or in fast forward? Why?

MAY 15

If you could make up a new holiday, what
would it be? What are some of the ways
people would celebrate it?

MAY 16

Think about a time when you felt happy.
What was going on and who were you with?

MAY 17

If you had friends all over the world,
how would you keep in touch?

MAY 18

If one of your classmates could be
the teacher for one day, who would
you want it to be and why?

MAY 19

If you could create one rule that
everyone in the world had to follow,
what rule would you create and why?

MAY 20

What makes your friends so awesome?

MAY 21

Would you rather be alone or
with friends? Why?

MAY 22

What does it mean to be a good person?
Which habits and values does a good person have?

MAY 23

What do you think adults spend their
money on that is wasteful?

MAY 24

If you could have any animal as a pet, which
animal would you choose and why?

MAY 25

What makes you feel brave? Explain.

MAY 26

If you could change one family rule, which
rule would you change and why?

MAY 27

Would you rather always feel like you
have to sneeze or that you are always
being tickled? Why?

MAY 28

What is the best birthday present you
ever received? Who gave it to you?

MAY 29

If you had the chance to be the teacher
tomorrow, what would you teach your class?
Would you take them on a field trip?
If so, where would you go?

MAY 30

Who is your favorite musician or band?
What do you love about their music?

MAY 31

What positive habit can you create that
will give you more self-esteem?

Family time should be prioritized and protected.

6

JUNE

JUNE 1

Would you rather listen to music or read a book? What kind of music do you like to have on in the background when you are in the car?

JUNE 2

When you are sick and not feeling well, what are some things you like to do?

JUNE 3

What are five things you want to do this summer? How can we make these happen?
Tip: As a family, make a list or chart and post it somewhere visible like the kitchen or family room. Check things off as you go to see how many you can get through!

JUNE 4

What is something you can do if you are struggling with a specific subject in school?

JUNE 5

What are some of the best things about being outside in nature?

JUNE 6

Before cell phones, television, and video games existed, what activities and things did people do during their free time?

JUNE 7

Would you rather have a car that flies or
one that goes underwater? Why?

JUNE 8

What do you think heaven is going to be like?

JUNE 9

What do you think your first job will be?
How much money do you hope to make?

JUNE 10

If you could give $500 to a cause,
which cause would you choose?
Examples: animals, children, education,
disability, elderly, environment, etc.

JUNE 11

What are some behaviors that are never
okay and should not be accepted?

JUNE 12

If you could be insanely talented at one thing,
which talent would you choose and why?

JUNE 13

What is something that makes
our family special?

JUNE 14

Would you rather live in Antarctica
or outer space for a year? What would
you bring with you?

JUNE 15

What makes you feel loved by others? Explain.

JUNE 16

Would you cheat on a test if you knew you would not get caught? Why or why not?

JUNE 17

What is your favorite thing about summertime? Explain.

JUNE 18

If you had to give away all of your toys, who would you give them to and why?

JUNE 19

What is the best gift you have ever given? Why was it so special?

JUNE 20

When do you feel motivated and confident? What are you doing? Who are you with?

JUNE 21

Would you rather eat all hot foods or all cold foods? What would be on the menu?

JUNE 22

Do you like mornings better or
nights better? Why?

JUNE 23

Who in our family is the funniest?
What makes this person so funny?

JUNE 24

Do you think you will go to college?
Which college do you want to attend?

JUNE 25

What are some activities and games
on cell phones, iPads, or other devices
that are inappropriate?

JUNE 26

What is your most embarrassing moment?
Will you share the story?

JUNE 27

Would you rather camp in a tent under
the stars or in an RV? Why?

JUNE 28

How do you show others you
care about them?

JUNE 29

What is one thing you really want
to buy but cannot afford?

JUNE 30

What do you want to be when
you grow up and why?

Connection is the energy that is created between people when they feel seen, heard, and valued.

– Brené Brown

JULY 7

JULY 1

Would you rather get to eat whatever you want, whenever you want, or go to bed whenever you want? What time do you think you should go to bed?

JULY 2

If someone is not able to donate their money to a good cause, what are some things they could do to still be a part of the cause?

JULY 3

If you could meet anyone, alive or dead, who would you choose and why?

JULY 4

What is your favorite part of
celebrating the 4th of July?

JULY 5

What is the best thing about your best friend?

JULY 6

What is one book you have read that you
loved? Why did you love it so much?

JULY 7

Would you rather have a swimming pool or an
amazing treehouse in your backyard? Why?

JULY 8

Are there any worries or fears that you
need to talk to God about? What are they?
*Tip: If your children are not comfortable sharing their
answers, ask them when can they set aside time with
God to talk about their worries and fears.*

JULY 9

If you were granted one wish, what
would it be and why?

JULY 10

What does it feel like when
someone hugs you?

JULY 11

How can you make sure you are
physically and emotionally healthy?

JULY 12

What is something you look
forward to all day? Explain.

JULY 13

If our family was going to start a new
weekly or monthly tradition, what tradition
do you think we should start?

JULY 14

Would you rather be able to talk with animals
or speak every foreign language? Why?

JULY 15

Do you prefer going to the beach
or a pool? Explain.

JULY 16

What is your earliest memory?

JULY 17

How do you think going to school
helps you achieve your dreams?

JULY 18

Do you think that what we watch on television
impacts our feelings, friendships, and ideas?
Why or why not?

JULY 19

Do you ever get sad for no reason? If so, what are you thinking about in those moments?

JULY 20

Why do you think it is important for adults and kids to have a role model or mentor in their life?

JULY 21

Would you rather receive gifts or do something fun on your birthday? Why?

JULY 22

If you could choose any way to spend a family night at home, what would you want us to do?

JULY 23

Do you think you will get married one day and if so, at what age?

JULY 24

Why do you think some people are very generous with their valuables and money?

JULY 25

Which person in your life is your exact opposite? What makes you so different?

JULY 26

What are you thankful for? Explain.

JULY 27

So far, which teacher has been your favorite and why?

JULY 28

Would you rather win an Olympic gold medal
or win a million dollars in the lottery?
What sport would you play in the Olympics?

JULY 29

Right now, what is the funniest thing
you can think of? Why is it so funny?

JULY 30

In our family, who is the most energetic?
What kinds of things does this person do?

JULY 31

If you could change one thing about
the world, what would it be?

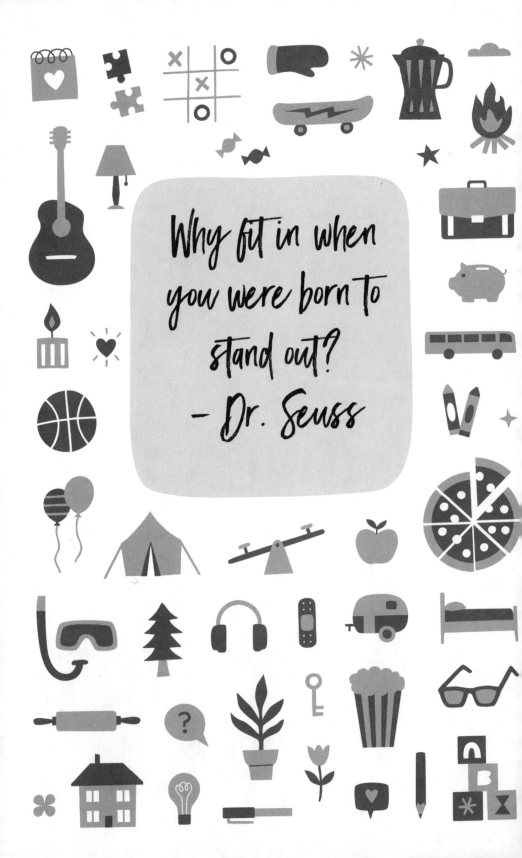

8

AUGUST

AUGUST 1

Would you rather have to sew all your clothes
or grow your own food? Why?

AUGUST 2

Who is your favorite sports or movie star right
now? What makes this person special?

AUGUST 3

If you were given $1,000, what
would you buy with the money?

AUGUST 4

If you could write a book about anything, what would it be about and what would you title it?

AUGUST 5

What is something you did today that you would love to do every day?

AUGUST 6

When you feel angry, what are some ways you can calm yourself down?

AUGUST 7

Would you rather have nosy neighbors
or noisy neighbors? Explain.

AUGUST 8

Which five words best describe summer?

AUGUST 9

If you could build anything outside or
in the backyard, what would it be?

AUGUST 10

Who in our family is the quietest?
Why do you think this person is quiet?

AUGUST 11

What are some simple ways you
can include others around you?

AUGUST 12

What would you do with your time
if you had all technology taken away
from you for an entire week?

AUGUST 13

What do you think the worst smell
in the world is and why?

AUGUST 14

Would you rather be too busy to do anything
or be bored all the time? Why?

AUGUST 15

Do you think cheating on your homework or
on a test is wrong even if you know it will help
you pass the class? Why or why not?

AUGUST 16

What do you think is the most
important rule to follow and why?

AUGUST 17

What is a memory that makes you feel happy?

AUGUST 18

If you started your own company, what service
or product would you provide? What would
you name your company?

AUGUST 19

Can you name three people who are really
funny? What makes them so funny?

AUGUST 20

If you could only eat one
food every day for the rest of your life,
what would it be and why?

AUGUST 21

Would you rather watch a sports
game at home on a big screen TV or
be live at the stadium? What is your
favorite team to watch play?

AUGUST 22

Have you ever been pressured by your friends
to do something you are not comfortable
with? What happened?

AUGUST 23

What are some technology
boundaries our family should have?

AUGUST 24

What do you think is the greatest invention
of all time? What makes it so great?

AUGUST 25

In our family, who is the most opinionated?
What makes this person so opinionated?

AUGUST 26

If you had your own country, what would it be
called? What would your flag look like?

AUGUST 27

What makes you feel insecure?
How do you handle your insecurities?

AUGUST 28

Would you rather spend the day
with your favorite athlete or your
favorite musician? Why?

AUGUST 29

What activities do you enjoy
doing with your friends?

AUGUST 30

If you could add one new subject
to your school's curriculum, what
would it be and why?

AUGUST 31

If you had to give away any five things
in our house, what would they be and
why would you choose them?

SEPTEMBER

SEPTEMBER 1

What are ways you would like us
to celebrate your birthday?

SEPTEMBER 2

What would you like to learn how to do?
What would you do with this new ability?

SEPTEMBER 3

Where do you want us to go on our
next family vacation and why?

SEPTEMBER 4

When did you feel most proud
of yourself this week?

SEPTEMBER 5

What do you like to do
during recess and lunch?

SEPTEMBER 6

What is the hardest thing you have ever had
to do? What made it so difficult?

SEPTEMBER 7

Would you rather be poor and work at a job you are passionate about, or rich and work at a job you absolutely cannot stand? Why?

SEPTEMBER 8

What do you think is the coolest thing God created and why?

SEPTEMBER 9

How many times a day do you think about doing something nice for someone else? What would it take for you to act on one of those ideas?

SEPTEMBER 10

If you were given five million dollars
to help others in need, how would
you spend the money?

SEPTEMBER 11

If you could invent something for
the future, what would it be and
what purpose would it serve?

SEPTEMBER 12

As a family, how can we make you
feel more loved and special?

SEPTEMBER 13

What is your least favorite
subject in school and why?

SEPTEMBER 14

Would you rather have your flight delayed by
eight hours or lose your luggage? Why?

SEPTEMBER 15

What is the nicest thing someone has done
for you? What made it so special?

SEPTEMBER 16

What are some things you can do to protect
your privacy while being on a cell phone?
Examples: complex passwords, don't leave your
phone unattended, be cautious with what you
post on social media, etc.

SEPTEMBER 17

How does it make you feel when
your friends exclude you?

SEPTEMBER 18

If you could invent any sport,
what would it be and what would you call it?

SEPTEMBER 19

Do you think we show any favoritism
in our family? If so, how?

SEPTEMBER 20

What is your favorite thing about fall? Explain.

SEPTEMBER 21

Would you rather go without TV or junk
food for the rest of your life? Why?

SEPTEMBER 22

What is one thing you look forward to
when you become an adult? Explain.

SEPTEMBER 23

Do you know anyone at your school who has
experienced cyberbullying? Why do you think
so many students use the internet and social
media to bully others?

SEPTEMBER 24

Should you give money to a homeless person
on the street? Why or why not?

SEPTEMBER 25

What do you do when a friend does not
follow through with a promise?

SEPTEMBER 26

What is your favorite dessert of all time?
Who makes the best one or where
can you buy it?

SEPTEMBER 27

What makes you really angry?
What do you do when you are really angry?

SEPTEMBER 28

What was the most creative thing
you did this month?

SEPTEMBER 29

What is one thing you would do to
change our home and why?

SEPTEMBER 30

Who is someone at your school that would
appreciate more kindness and compassion?

No act of kindness, no matter how small, is ever wasted.

10

OCTOBER

OCTOBER 1

Would you rather get to skip
whatever class you wanted every single
day or get as much screen time as you
wanted on the weekends? Why?

OCTOBER 2

If we could go on a camping trip this
month, where would you like to go
and what should we bring?

OCTOBER 3

Do you feel comfortable asking for
help when you are unsure about something?
Why or why not?

OCTOBER 4

If you had to leave home because of an emergency, which four things would you take with you?

OCTOBER 5

If you could dress up like any character for Halloween, who would you choose and why?

OCTOBER 6

What do you miss about being little?

OCTOBER 7

Would you rather ace every single test you took without studying or win every single sports game you played? Why?

OCTOBER 8

How has God blessed you? What are some things in your life that you can thank him for?

OCTOBER 9

Do you think it is safe to use a cell phone while driving? Why or why not?

OCTOBER 10

Is there anyone at school who gets bullied or made fun of often? Is there anything you can do to help the situation?

OCTOBER 11

When was the last time you cried? What did you cry about?

OCTOBER 12

If you went back in time, how far back would you go and what would you do when you got there?

OCTOBER 13

Which five words best describe fall?

OCTOBER 14

Is there anything that someone in our family needs to apologize for?

OCTOBER 15

What does it mean to be generous with your money?

OCTOBER 16

If you could invent an app, what would
it do? What would you call it?

OCTOBER 17

If you could be principal for one week,
what are some things you would change?
What are some things you would incorporate?

OCTOBER 18

What is the most amazing true
story you have ever heard?

OCTOBER 19

Do you ever feel like people are too busy for you? How does that make you feel?

OCTOBER 20

What is something you have to do every day, but do not like doing?

OCTOBER 21

Many men and women from all around the world volunteer themselves to serve in their country's military. What do you think they hope to accomplish by serving their country? Why do you think they make such a big decision?

OCTOBER 22

What is a new holiday tradition you
would like to start this year?

OCTOBER 23

What is the most expensive thing you
have broken? How did it break?

OCTOBER 24

Why do you think some people are very
stingy with their money and resources?

OCTOBER 25

Do you think it is important to have a "no cell phone" rule during our family dinners? Why or why not?

OCTOBER 26

What are some ways that we can stay more organized around the house?

OCTOBER 27

What invention does not get a lot of attention, but has greatly improved the world?

OCTOBER 28

When you are not feeling well, do you like to be left alone or does having others around you help cheer you up? Explain.

OCTOBER 29

What do you like least about doing group projects at school?

OCTOBER 30

What are some of your top strengths?

OCTOBER 31

If you were to invent a candy bar,
which ingredients would you use and
what would you name it?

Staying vulnerable
is a risk we have to take
if we want to experience
connection.
— Brené Brown

NOVEMBER 1

What is your favorite thing that Mom
or Dad makes for lunch?

NOVEMBER 2

What is a new Thanksgiving tradition you
would like our family to do?

NOVEMBER 3

If you see someone who always sits alone at
school, how could you be friendly to that person?
What would make it difficult to do that?
Examples: peer pressure, fear of how the
person will respond, etc.

NOVEMBER 4

Do you think kids should get their own
cell phone based off of their age or by how
responsible they are? Explain.

NOVEMBER 5

When it comes to voting, what values
are most important to keep in mind?

NOVEMBER 6

What makes you happy when you feel sad?

NOVEMBER 7

Would you rather have an action-packed
vacation in Europe or spend time relaxing and
swimming at the beach in Hawaii? Why?

NOVEMBER 8

Did anyone do anything super nice
for you this week? Explain.

NOVEMBER 9

What is your favorite part of the school day?

NOVEMBER 10

What are some practical ways, as a family, we all can give back
to our community during this holiday season?
*Tip: Brainstorm a few volunteer opportunities and
write them down. Take the time to look into ways
your family could serve together.*

NOVEMBER 11

If you could shrink down to the size
of an ant, what would you do?

NOVEMBER 12

When you think of generosity, which person
or character comes to mind? Explain.

NOVEMBER 13

What is your favorite part of our home?
Examples: the family room, the backyard, the
smell of delicious food, your cozy bed, etc.

NOVEMBER 14

Would you rather be the funniest person in
the room or the most intelligent? Why?

NOVEMBER 15

What does it mean to be a bad person?
What habits and values does a bad person have?

NOVEMBER 16

What is the weirdest dream
you have had lately?

NOVEMBER 17

Have you ever tried to make something
in the kitchen and it turned out terrible?
What happened?

NOVEMBER 18

The opposite of being thankful is being entitled. Someone who
is entitled has unrealistic demands or expectations of others,
what they deserve, or how they should be treated. What does
it feel like to be around someone that acts entitled? What are
some ways you can make sure you do not act entitled?

NOVEMBER 19

What problem do you hope to solve in your lifetime? What will you need to learn in order to solve this problem?

NOVEMBER 20

If someone donated one million dollars to your school, how would you want the staff and teachers to spend the money?

NOVEMBER 21

If you could live anywhere in the world for one year, where would you live and why?

NOVEMBER 22

Why do you think that it is important
for a person to know that they are
loved and valued?

NOVEMBER 23

What is one thing you can do when you
have a bad attitude to turn it around?

NOVEMBER 24

Since Thanksgiving often reminds
us to be thankful for what we have,
what are three things you are thankful for?
Who are three people you are thankful for?

NOVEMBER 25

On a scale of 1-10 (1=sad, 10=happy),
how would you rate your general
feelings as a person?

NOVEMBER 26

Have you ever played a joke on someone?
What did you do? How did the person react?

NOVEMBER 27

What is something you are working
on at school right now?

NOVEMBER 28

How do you handle disagreements and
conflicts with your friends?

NOVEMBER 29

What are two things that
frustrate you? Explain.

NOVEMBER 30

Many people buy things they want
but cannot afford, so they use credit cards.
Do you think it is okay to spend money you do not
have? What are some things that can go wrong
with this kind of spending?

If you want to feel rich, just count all the gifts you have that money can't buy.

12

DECEMBER

DECEMBER 1

Who made you smile this week?
How did that person make you smile?

DECEMBER 2

Do you enjoy wrapping presents, going
Christmas shopping, and decorating a
Christmas tree? Explain.

DECEMBER 3

If you could go on a date with your parents,
where would you go and what would you do?

DECEMBER 4

When are the best days and times for
our family to be technology-free?

DECEMBER 5

Which shows on TV do you think are worth
your time? Which ones do you think are not
worth your time watching?

DECEMBER 6

What is an academic challenge that
you have to overcome?

DECEMBER 7

Would you rather sing a song in
front of complete strangers or your
closest friends? Why?

DECEMBER 8

Do you feel like God is always with you or
only with you some of the time? Explain.

DECEMBER 9

Which movie is coming out that
you really want to see?
Who would you like to see it with?

DECEMBER 10

During winter break, what are two
things you want to do as a family?

DECEMBER 11

When you are feeling stuck or
confused, do you have a hard time
asking for help? Explain.

DECEMBER 12

What do you think will be the most
difficult part about being an adult? Explain.

DECEMBER 13

Why do you think some kids are spoiled?
How did they become spoiled? Do you know
any kids that are spoiled?

DECEMBER 14

Would you rather win $50,000 or let your
best friend win $500,000? Why?

DECEMBER 15

What is something you can do to earn money right now?
Examples: dog walking, babysitting, chores around the house,
mowing the neighbor's yard, getting a job, etc.

DECEMBER 16

What do you like best about doing
group projects at school?

DECEMBER 17

Which movie can you watch over and
over again and never get sick of?

DECEMBER 18

What was the funniest thing
that happened today?

DECEMBER 19

Do you have any friends who are
obsessed with technology?
How do you know that they are obsessed?

DECEMBER 20

What is something new you would like
to learn more about and why?

DECEMBER 21

What is your favorite thing about
winter? Explain.

DECEMBER 22

What was something nice you did for
someone else this month?

DECEMBER 23

What is one compliment you have
received from someone that made a
lasting impact on your life?

DECEMBER 24

What does Christmas spirit mean to you?
What is your favorite way to celebrate it?

DECEMBER 25

What is the best Christmas gift you have
ever received? Who gave it to you?

DECEMBER 26

Pick one person in our family to
do an impression of: Dad, Mom, one
of your siblings, or your pet.

DECEMBER 27

What is your favorite tradition we do
as a family during the holidays?

DECEMBER 28

Do you like to read fiction or
nonfiction books? Explain.

DECEMBER 29

What is your favorite thing that Mom
or Dad makes for breakfast?

DECEMBER 30

What is something that you are
worried about? What is it that you
think is going to happen?

DECEMBER 31

What intention would you like to set for yourself in the new year? Are you going to write it down somewhere?

You are capable of so much more than you can imagine.

BLENDED FAMILY QUESTIONS

QUESTIONS FOR BLENDED FAMILIES

The following questions can be fun, informative, and thought-provoking. As a parent and stepparent, you must also be prepared for hard and hurtful answers from your children. Don't retaliate. Don't try to justify. Just listen. Listen to their feelings and encourage them to be open and honest. Seek to understand their hearts and minds. Blending a family from other family fragments is difficult, but a gentle listening ear is an amazing glue that will begin to bind your family together!

While every blended family has its own unique dynamics, take the following questions and customize them as needed. If a question is not relevant, just skip it and move on to the next one.

- There are many difficult things about having to live in two separate homes, but sometimes there are perks too! What are some of the benefits you get from living in two homes?

- Do you think you should have to do chores when you are at your other parent's house? What about at our house? Explain.

- Volunteering is a great way to serve and share with others who are less fortunate. How would you like to volunteer as a family? What causes are you passionate about?

- We know it has to be difficult living in two different homes. What are some of the challenges you face living in two places?

- What has been the hardest part of this new marriage and blended family for you? How can we make it better?

- When we have family fun night, what are some activities you think we should do?

- If you have step siblings, do you ever feel excluded or unnoticed when they are playing together? How does that make you feel? Is there anything we can do to make it better?

- How does it make you feel knowing your Mom and Dad are not married anymore? *Remember parents, make this a safe place for your children to share their honest emotions!*

- What can we *(biological parent and stepparent)* do to help you stay connected to your other biological parent while you are with us?

- What is something **(stepparent's name)** could do to have a closer relationship with you?

- What could **(biological parent's name)** do to make life easier, less stressful, or more fun?

- What are some positive things that **(stepparent's name)** has brought to our blended family?

- Sometimes your two homes have different religions and beliefs. What is the greatest struggle you have in trying to be a part of each family's belief system? How can we better support you and your freedom to choose your own beliefs?

- Everyone needs to feel loved and included in this blended family. How can we make **(stepparent's name)** feel like a part of our family? How can we make **(step siblings)** feel like a part of this family? How can we better blend all the children together in our family?

- What do you miss most about our old family traditions during the holidays? What could our new blended family do to incorporate some of the past while still creating new family traditions?

- Holidays, birthdays, and special events can be challenging when you are living in two separate homes. How can we help you stay connected during those special times when you are apart from your other family gatherings and celebrations?

Tip: You could also ask the children if they would like for you to help them buy presents, cards, or other items for the family members they don't get to see on holidays.

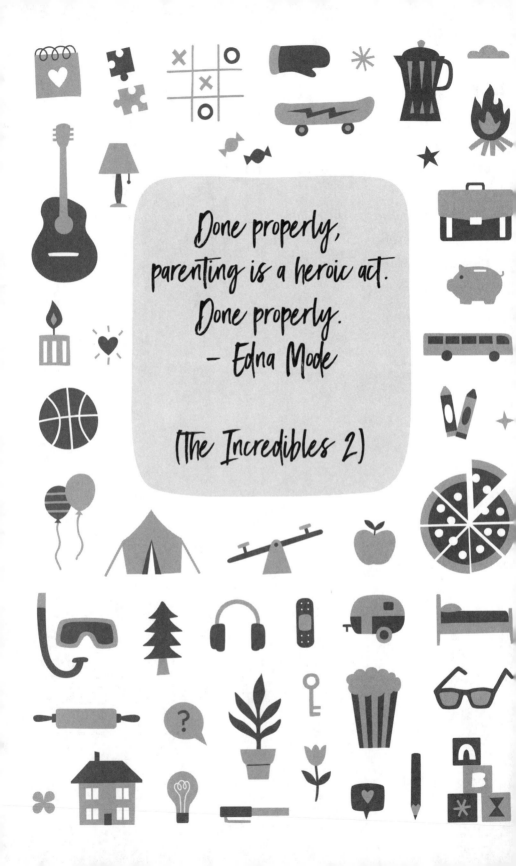

Done properly,
parenting is a heroic act.
Done properly.
— Edna Mode

(The Incredibles 2)

HOW ARE YOU
FEELING?

INDEX

CHARACTER AND VALUES

Jan 2, 30, 31 // **Feb** 11, 26 // **Mar** 13, 25, 31 // **Apr** 19, 24, 29 //
May 2, 3, 12, 22, 31 // **Jun** 11, 16, 20 // **Jul** 11, 20 // **Aug** 11, 15,
22 // **Sept** 9, 23, 30 // **Oct** 21, 30 // **Nov** 3, 15, 22, 23, 25 //
Dec 13, 22

FAITH AND SPIRITUALITY

Jan 8 // **Mar** 8 // **Apr** 8 // **May** 8 // **Jun** 8 // **Jul** 8 // **Sept** 8 //
Oct 8 // **Dec** 8

FAMILY AND FRIENDS

Jan 1, 9, 15, 18, 26, 27 // **Feb** 6, 15, 22 // **Mar** 2, 11, 19, 25, 30
// **Apr** 9, 19, 30 // **May** 2, 13, 20, 26 // **Jun** 13, 23, 28 // **Jul**
5, 13, 22, 30 // **Aug** 10, 19, 22, 23, 25, 29 // **Sept** 3, 12, 17, 19,
25, 29 // **Oct** 2, 14, 26 // **Nov** 1, 13, 28 // **Dec** 3, 26, 29

FEELINGS AND EMOTIONS

Jan 4, 13, 26 // **Feb** 2, 12, 24 // **Mar** 6, 18, 26 // **Apr** 5, 12, 27
// **May** 4, 16, 22, 25 // **Jun** 2, 15, 28 // **Jul** 10, 18, 19, 26 // **Aug**
6, 17, 27 // **Sept** 4, 17, 27 // **Oct** 3, 11, 19, 28 // **Nov** 6, 15, 29 //
Dec 11, 23, 30

HOLIDAYS AND SEASONS

Jan 10 // **Feb** 8, 28 // **Mar** 4 // **Apr** 18 // **May** 15, 28 // **Jun** 3, 17 // **Jul** 4, 15 // **Aug** 8 // **Sept** 1, 21 // **Oct** 5, 13, 22 // **Nov** 2, 10, 18, 24 // **Dec** 2, 10, 21, 24, 25, 27, 31

JUST FOR FUN

Jan 5, 9, 12, 16, 17, 19, 20, 22, 24, 29 // **Feb** 3, 9, 10, 13, 17, 18, 20, 23, 27 // **Mar** 5, 10, 15, 17, 20, 23, 27, 29 // **Apr** 3, 4, 6, 11, 13, 17, 20, 22, 25, 28 // **May** 5, 10, 15, 17, 19, 24, 30 // **Jun** 5, 9, 12, 19, 22, 26, 30 // **Jul** 3, 9, 12, 16, 23, 25, 29, 31 // **Aug** 2, 5, 9, 13, 16, 20, 24, 26 // **Sept** 2, 6, 11, 15, 18, 22, 26, 28 // **Oct** 4, 6, 12, 16, 18, 20, 23, 27, 31 // **Nov** 5, 8, 11, 16, 17, 19, 21, 26 // **Dec** 1, 9, 12, 17, 18, 20

MONEY AND GIVING

Jan 6, 23 // **Feb** 10, 19 // **Mar** 9, 22 // **Apr** 3, 15 // **May** 9, 23 // **Jun** 10, 18, 29 // **Jul** 2, 24 // **Aug** 3, 18, 31 // **Sept** 10, 24 // **Oct** 15, 24 // **Nov** 12, 20, 30 // **Dec** 14, 15

SCHOOL AND LEARNING

Jan 3, 11, 25, 31 // **Feb** 4, 16, 25 // **Mar** 3, 12, 24 // **Apr** 2, 16, 23, 29 // **May** 6, 18, 29 // **Jun** 4, 16, 24 // **Jul** 6, 17, 27 // **Aug** 4, 15, 30 // **Sept** 2, 5, 13, 23, 30 // **Oct** 10, 17, 29 // **Nov** 3, 9, 20, 27 // **Dec** 6, 16, 20, 28

TECHNOLOGY

Jan 4, 19 // **Feb** 5, 18 // **Mar** 16 // **Apr** 10, 21, 26 // **May** 11 // **Jun** 6, 25 // **Jul** 18 // **Aug** 12, 23 // **Sept** 16 // **Oct** 9, 16, 25 // **Nov** 4 // **Dec** 5

WOULD YOU RATHER

Jan 7, 14, 21, 28 // **Feb** 1, 7, 14, 21 // **Mar** 1, 7, 14, 21, 28 // **Apr** 1, 7, 14, 21 // **May** 1, 7, 14, 21, 27 // **Jun** 1, 7, 14, 21, 27 // **Jul** 1, 7, 14, 21, 28 // **Aug** 1, 7, 14, 21, 28 // **Sept** 7, 14, 21 // **Oct** 1, 7 // **Nov** 7, 14 // **Dec** 7, 14

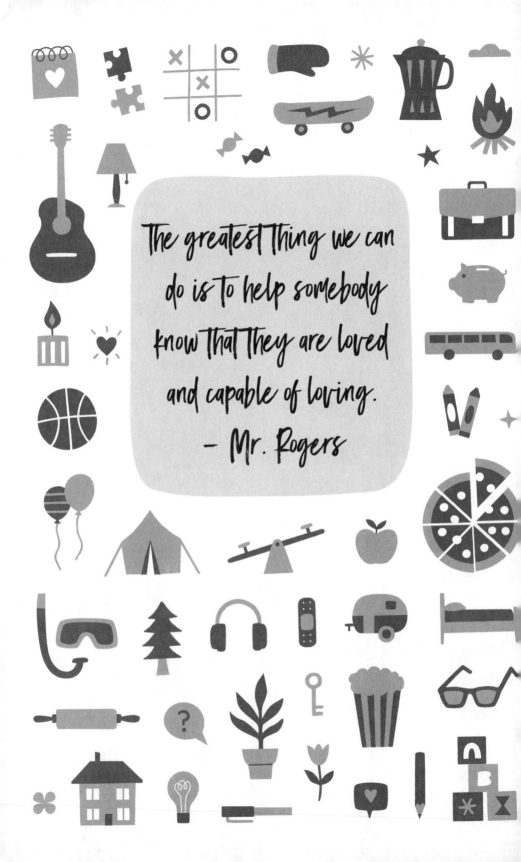

The greatest thing we can do is to help somebody know that they are loved and capable of loving.

– Mr. Rogers

ABOUT
MARRIAGE365

Known as the couple least likely to succeed, Casey and Meygan Caston faced every obstacle imaginable on their way to happily ever after. Not wanting to become part of the next divorce statistic, they began educating themselves and learning how to do marriage the right way. They started sharing relationship and marriage tips on social media in 2013 and quickly learned that they weren't alone. Once they realized how many other couples were also trying to pursue healthy marriages and in desperate need of practical tools, Casey and Meygan couldn't just sit back and watch.

Co-founding Marriage365 later that year, they have since nurtured a thriving online community that reaches millions of couples from seriously dating to newlyweds to relationships in crisis. They provide hope, healing, and happiness through resources like their free app, *My Marriage365*, which offers a marriage health assessment and delivers personalized content.

Marriage365 is a 501(c)(3) non-profit with a dream that one day healthy, connected married couples are the norm. Their mission is to help spark connection and create a better future for generations to come. Casey and Meygan live in Southern California and love spending time at the beach with their two children.

Follow **@marriage365** on social media or visit **marriage365.org** to learn more.

If you like this book, make sure to check our other titles in this series:

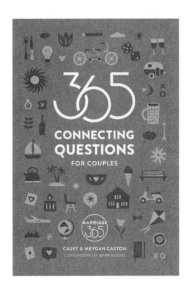

For Married Couples
(Also available in Spanish)

For Seriously Dating & Engaged Couples

To purchase a copy, go to marriage365.org/store